Two images dominated the city dawnscape. One was a small, bright helicopter speeding like a silver insect against the gaunt silhouettes of the city. The other was a soaring tower on the summit of which pulsed the huge neon number '23'. Above them both in the early light winked and twinkled the thousand satellites which cluttered the morning skies.

Inside the racing chopper Edison Carter, award winning reporter of Network 23's investigative *What I Want To Know Show*, adjusted the radio link of his video camera. It was the first assignment of his working day.

"This is Edison Carter to Network 23".

"Twenty-three to Edison Carter. We're trying to clear the link. We have some intermittent voice loss," crackled the receiver, heavy with early morning static. The pilot swooped down below the tops of the stark high buildings. "Twenty three to Edison Carter. We have you strong and clear. Your controller is Gorrister."

Inside the tower, headquarters of Network 23, on one of the hundreds of levels sat controller Gorrister. Today it was his job to guide Edison Carter to his target. Using the Sky Eye satellites he could place him anywhere on the face of the earth. He was his unseen eyes and ears. His guide and his protector.

"Hello Edison." Gorrister checked the television monitors before him, watching the precise print-outs which showed him Carter's exact location second by second.

"Right, you are above the incident. Descend and I'll control you in."

Perhaps it was the fact that today's incident was so local, so seemingly straightforward, that Gorrister was so relaxed. He lit another cigarette.

"How long before we're on air?" Carter's voice asked urgently.

"Thirty seconds. Relax ... we'll make it."

Across the long room packed with controllers Gorrister watched the producer, Murray, cut up the programme logo. Gorrister punched up Carter's transmit button.

Using his camera Edison transmitted his own picture down to the network receivers.

"This is Edison Carter, live and direct, asking the questions you want answered. Right now what I want to know is – just what happened in Apartment 42 in the last sixty minutes? Just what is it that someone doesn't want us to know?"

Carter's catch-phrase was famous; 'What I Want to Know' had become the common currency of enquiry.

"Come with me now," he continued above the shake and roar of the descending chopper, "let's go get some answers".

It was a dramatic, self-consciously jazzy introduction. It was designed to be, for every day and every night the Networks battled to seize and hold the viewers.

"Hey Edison," Gorrister's voice crackled, "you've got competition. There's quite a scene down there".

He glanced at his screens. His hand moved across the littered desk to select 'deep focus' on his panel. The satellite picture cut closer and closer, the edge of the continent giving way to the city, the streets and finally a single doorway in a single building.

The radio-distorted voice of Edison Carter

returned. There was an edge of impatience.

"Isn't it about time I had control?"

Gorrister grunted and s

"Picture good. Balance and strong. I'm cutting up t Carter was carrying his car. The picture was clear. It see ground, its eye noting the d streets, now and then catching darting, furtive figures. Carter was in one part of the vast dereliction that was the city. In this dangerous world Gorrister was more than a trained technician handling the battered but complex machinery of the great satellite links. He was at Carter's side – ahead, behind and above him. Whatever Carter's camera saw was transmitted back to Gorrister. It was this that could keep Carter, or any of his fellow reporters, safe. And there was not an essential map or diagram that could not be accessed through the Network's computers and data stores.

Gorrister turned as he felt his producer at his shoulder.

"Gorrister, do we have an update on Carter's story?"

"All we have is that it's an explosion and that the area is sealed off to all but residents."

Murray nodded slowly and watched the screens.

"Why the hell does Carter want this story? He wondered. A trainee could handle it."

Gorrister had wondered the same thing. He didn't like Carter. He was good of course; the best reporter there was on any Network. But he was cold, unapproachable, at least to Gorrister. Other controllers liked him well enough but Gorrister had always found him too smart for his own good. He lit another cigarette and sat back.

Behind him the room buzzed as earnest, tense faces peered at their screens and guided their reporters in the field.

"Ted, your position is getting very hot. I have troop movements close to your right. I'm putting a chopper in to you."

The controller traced the reporter's position with his cursor. He spoke swift instructions to a pilot 8,000 miles away. Beyond him another controller hunched over his desk.

"Your satellite will be over the horizon in two-five seconds", while another, arms raised in horror yelled "Annie I *know* it's an important interview but you can't just smash the window in. I mean, holy shit, it's the Vatican."

Gorrister turned away, dropping his cigarette in his coffee cup. He watched his screens then spoke into his head set.

"Edison, I'm sending you in on the east side. I'm getting infra red on the main entrance. I guess that's security."

"OK control," crackled Edisor Carter's voice, "I'm going in as advised."As Edison Carter's camera revealed pictures of the entrance and concrete stairs of Apartment Block 84B, Gorrister watched the screen. Like Carter, he heard the morning television shows ebb and flow as the doors passed by ... "Mr Beefies Bisonburger injected at source with all the relishes ... Hello Nyasaland welcome to global Song of the Century..." The camera swung up the stairs of the

NETWORK 23
4516805976
WHAT I WANT TO KNOW SHOW

dreadful, spiritless ghetto. A huge distorted face filled the screen as a woman stared into the camera as she bent to collect something from the floor ... 'Asian Premier Kysoty reports full foodbanks for the next quarter ... and now from Zikzak, the world's biggest corporation, comes 'Musquash', a combined fly-killer and deodorant...'

"Gorrister, do we have an update?"

"Not really," responded Gorrister. "Apparently the wife's been hospitalised. Murray's trying for a newslink interview. Turn right at the end, then left and the apartment is .. about .. seven down on the right."

"OK control."

Edison Carter was edgy. The normal banter between controller and reporter gave a frail warmth to the electronic umbilical that joined a reporter to base. Gorrister wasn't like that. Edison remembered an uncomplimentary quotation and grinned. He had one of those grins that comes unbidden from a stern, intelligent face. But his mind was aways one small step ahead of his body and had shut down the smile before it had left his face. Every instinct in him had detected something. Where the hell was Gorrister? What was round the corner?

Had Gorrister not been borrowing a cigarette he would have seen on his screens the three infra red glowpoints round the corner. He would also have seen Edison's camera's view of the guard at the door and the two reporters, cameras at the shoulder, smiling helplessly at Edison.

"This man says through here we no go," mimicked one.

"Hi Patrick," said Edison.

"Typical, the first time we get a story before you and control has pulled us out." moaned Patrick

The two men moved away swiftly, talking to their controllers their voices echoing away down the corridor. Edison turned thoughtfully towards the silent, impassive figure of the guard, then he

moved round the corner, speaking low into the camera.

"Gorrister, Gorrister! I'm calling you on the link. How come this story has been pulled?"

"It just came down to Murray," he snapped, "come on in."

Carter's voice, now hard, precise and clear, "I'm not dropping this one Gorrister. I'm going round the back to see if I can access a window".

At his desk Gorrister carried the resigned look of an old hand. He'd seen it all, he'd heard it all, he'd almost- done it all. With a great sigh he bent over his desk and reached for the switch.

"Edison. It's pulled. Come on in."

He snapped the switch off. His screens blanked out. He swung away into a comfortable position and turned to the next page of his morning schedule.

He heard the voice of Murray speaking to a controller in another bay.

"Ted, cut up your story on five. Continuity, cover me with a crosslink. OK."

In the shadow of Block 84B, Edison yelled into his camera, "Gorrister! Gorrister! You asshole."

But Gorrister heard nothing, neither did he see the two figures move through the shadows towards his reporter.

Edison was studying the window of the guarded apartment as the two derelicts approached. A curtain blew fitfully in the wind. The scorched surround was smeared and smoke stained. He was about to move closer when the manic yells of his assailants erupted. He swung around, instinct carrying his camera like a weapon. The nearest derelict caught it squarely and went down, but his partner fought wildly for the precious camera. He landed two blows then, shifting balance tripped and went down with his camera. Momentarily dazed his head buzzed ... it took some moments for him to realise that the hammering sound in his head was the chopper coming to his aid.

The picture book of the film
written by
Steve Roberts

A CORGI BOOK 0 552 99221 6
First publication in Great Britain

PRINTING HISTORY
Corgi edition published 1985
Copyright © 1985 Chrysalis Visual Programming Ltd.

This book is set in Futura Light by Keyline Graphics, London.

Corgi Books are published by Transworld Publishers Ltd.,
Century House, 61-63 Uxbridge Road, Ealing, London W5 5SA,
in Australia by Transworld Publishers (Aust.) Pty. Ltd.,
26 Harley Crescent, Condell Park, NSW 2200, and in
New Zealand by Transworld Publishers (N.Z.) Ltd., Cnr. Moselle
and Waipareira Avenues, Henderson, Auckland.

Made and Printed in Great Britain by Severn Valley Press.

Front cover photograph SHAUN CONROY-HARGRAVE
All other photographs BRIAN COOKE
Design BOUNCING BALL GRAPHICS

Edison Carter  Theora

Grosman  Bryce Lynch

Blank Reg  Dominique

Breughel  Mahler

Murray  Ben Cheviot

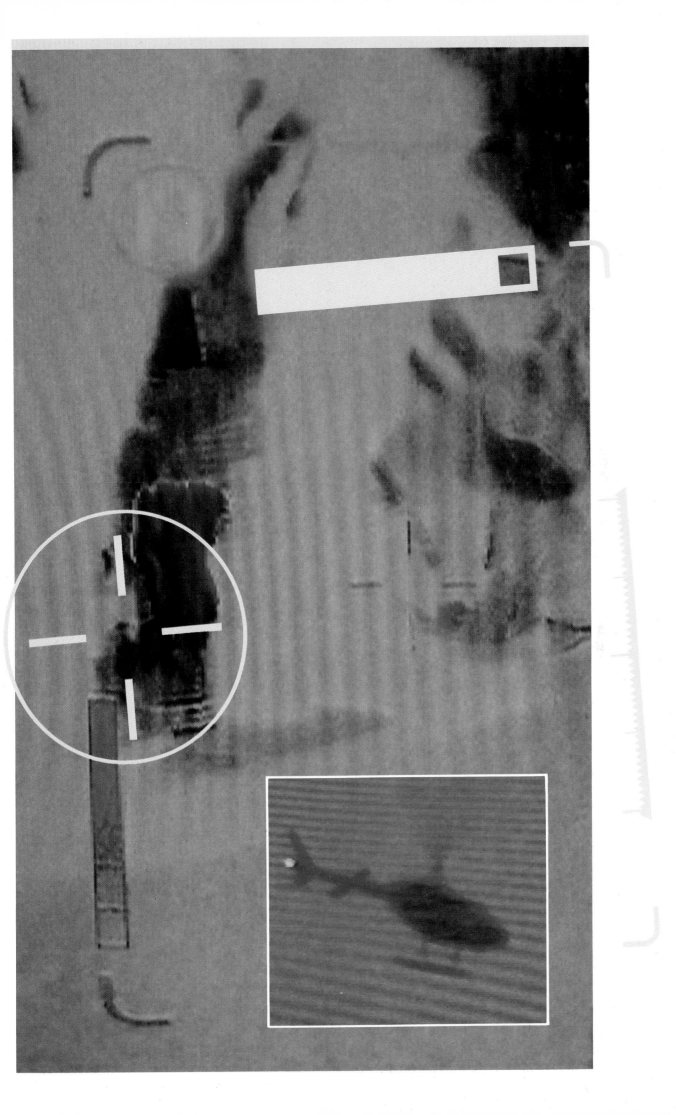

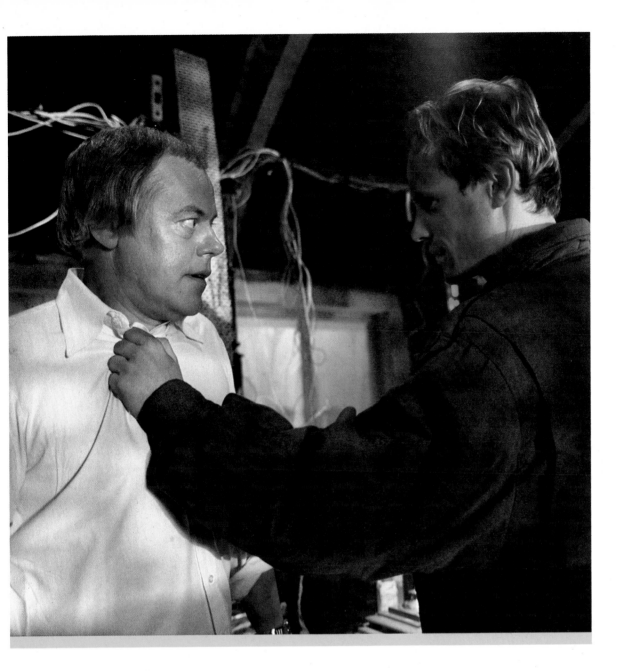

Murray turned from the screens as the heliport door smashed open. He moved towards Edison his hand raised in greeting until he saw Edison's head. It was gashed and blood still caked his cheek and forearm. Murray's hand hovered like a limp question mark. He turned to follow Edison, marching through the rows of gaping controllers. Murray hurried after him.

Gorrister was half standing as Edison punched him. He fell back into chair.

"You cut me off you lethal idot!"

"I pulled you. The job was pulled." Gorrister shouted between split lips.

"You cut me off! No job is over until I'm back at base."

Murray moved between them. "Hey Edison, what's the problem. Easy."

"The problem is that clown damn nearly got me killed," yelled Carter, moving towards Gorrister. Gorrister stood up and pushed past them towards the staring crowd.

"I don't need this prima-donna crap. Even from the great Edison bloody Carter," he growled as he stormed away.

At the end of the control room Carter stood, held firmly by Murray. His voice echoed after the retreating figure of Gorrister. "It's my ass out there, not yours."

Murray moved Edison aside as controllers went back to their consoles. Edison was not normally this explosive. Murray gestured calm.

"Murray, get him off me. Just get me a controller who can keep me alive out there. Get me the best."

"OK, OK," calmed Murray.

"The best!"

Murray winced, "Listen Edison, I was out there once. I know how you feel."

He paused. Both men knew he was right.

Edison watched Murray. Murray shifted uncomfortably. Edison relaxed and offered a hint of a smile. Murray took the bait and shrugged pleasantly. Then Edison struck.

"This is a big one, isn't it?"

"I don't know" said Murray. "It was pulled from high up."

Edison cocked his head. On the record and off the record they understood each other very well. Murray sighed, then looked hard at Carter.

"Very high," he said.

The Boardroom at Network 23 was located very high indeed.

Around a long rectangular table were spaced the six executives who guided Network 23 and at its head sat Grosman. He listened as the audience figures for the previous night's viewing were read out.

"Low at one hundred and fifteen million," intoned Edwards, "High at two hundred and thirty six million. That keeps us top network. Projections for the next hour are excellent." There was a ripple of satisfaction followed by a discussion of strategy. Grosman sat in reptilian silence.

He had just heard that his instruction to get Edison Carter off the Blipvert story had been carried out – but it had been dangerously close. It was imperative to act swiftly to prevent any further – 'inconvenience'. Grosman listened to Edward's smug litany of success.

"The Polly Show has good ratings and excellent holding. It's cheap, it's dumb and they love it."

Grosman cut in, all heads turning respectfully to his voice. "Let's turn to the Blipvert problem."

There was a murmur of assent. A signal or two of concern. Bryce, Network 23's Research and Development Head had developed a system for compressing conventional TV advertisements into a matter of seconds effectively stopping viewers channel switching. And, as there were several thousand channels to choose from, this was all too easy. The key to global success was to keep them once you had got them. And Blipverts did just that. They happened so fast nobody had time to activate their remote controls.

Only Network 23 had Blipverts. They had therefore captured the advertising account of the world's biggest corporation 'ZikZak'. It was a winning partnership.

There was however a problem, it was what Bryce had described as a 'side effect'. The executives had debated inconclusively.

"This is only the first generation to have viewed television constantly from birth", observed Ms Formby, "there may be some effect".

"Not our problem" snapped Edwards.

"Anyway we *want* them to watch all day. And night."

Ashwell, an ingratiating creature, poured syrup on troubled consciences.

"Good heavens" he chortled, "there may be no connection with Blipvertisements. Isolated incidences of this phenomenon occur throughout history. People sort of 'blow-up'. *You* know."

"No" replied the cold voice of Grosman, "I do not."

The evidence was mounting that in some way Blipverts caused certain people to explode.

Grosman had regarded the whole thing as a sick joke until he had seen the evidence on tape. Bryce had explained the technical reason, but Grosman had been too concerned about the negative effect on ratings to take much notice. And damn it, his own reporter Edison Carter had got too close to the story already.

Grosman was not amused by the irony that his own top man, a reporter who consistently got the channel top ratings for his investigative reporting, should reveal a story that could wreck Network 23.

The executives shifted uneasily as Grosman mused.

"I have asked the head of Research and Development to meet us on the videolink. Now he's our top man. Leave him absolutely to me."

The six faces turned to the wall screen.

It flickered and flashed. Then, hugely dominating the room, appeared the face of Bryce, the head of the Network's research facility.

"Hello there, Bryce," said Grosman winningly. "I need to talk to you about Blipverts."

Grosman's face featured what many people would have described as a smile. But it was an expression so removed from habit that the unused muscles soon gave up the struggle and it fell from his face. His eyes remained alert. Grosman's eyes never blinked.

But nobody was watching Grosman. They watched the screen with earnest attention and respect. They were looking at a genius. The face that had transformed the Network into the most powerful on earth.

They were used to the fact that he wore a T-shirt. They had even become accustomed to his spotty arrogance. But what, even now, gave them a feeling of discomfort was that the face staring at them, was that of a boy of sixteen.

"Well, I'm rather busy" lisped Bryce. "I have just succeeded in computer generating a parrot on screen. It squawks."

Executive eyes darted everywhere, hungrily hunting the correct response. It was only when Grosman, his smile craned back up to his face, said "My congratulations. Whatever next", that the generous, sycophancy of congratulation came from the executives.

"I wonder," ingratiated Grosman, "if you

could spare a moment to illustrate to the Board here this little hitch on Blipverts?"

Bryce groaned, fiddled off screen, and his image was replaced by a computer graphic of a typical consumer watching a television screen. "Well put simply", sighed Bryce, "the human body has millions of nerve endings. Each carries a tiny electrical charge, which, when added together becomes a surprisingly large charge. Normally people just burn it off. But in inactive people it just builds up. Now, because I designed Blipverts to compress thirty seconds of advertising, it appears that the brain violently stimulates these nerve endings *simultaneously*. In some subjects, this causes a short circuit. Some particularly slothful perpetual viewers literally explode. Simple as that."

There was a long, stunned silence. Bryce cheerfully continued, "I've got a rather good example of one on this Rebus Tape." Seven faces watched the screen, the effect was stunning.

Ben Cheviot was the first to react. "Simple!" It won't be simple when Blipverts go global. My God."

"Oh look here," chirped Edwards, "the only people who are that inactive are pensioners, the sick and the unemployed. And they have no spending power." The Boardroom was horribly silent. It was Grosman who spoke finally.

"Bryce, I take it that this Rebus Tape is in an extremely safe place?"

"Oh yes," said Bryce. "But you know it really isn't my problem. My brief was to stop channel switching. I mean I only invent the bomb – I don't drop it. Ha, ha!"

Bryce's little laugh spoke of a real nervousness. Brilliant as he was in his world of the computer he had no experience in human relationships. At the age of four, when his quite exceptional talents had been perceived, he had been sealed into Network 23's own school and there, remote from others, had arrived in the confused waters of adolescence without the insulating life jacket of a real childhood.

"Bryce," continued Grosman, "you see we're worried that it might affect sales if people started ... if they began to suspect that, er..."

Well don't tell them then," responded Bryce, with sharp logic.

"Unfortunately," Grosman went on, "one of our reporters may have got quite near the truth already. We must be careful." Bryce sighed. The answer was usually quite simple.

"Well fire him." he said. "Or you could always kill him."

For the first time that day Grosman's eyes blinked. Once.

Murray propelled the now showered and refreshed Edison through the control room. He was cheerful. He was hoping to lift Carter from the resonating bitterness of the Gorrister affair. He had 'stolen' Theora Jones from the World One programme and she was an ace controller. She also had a personality which might suit and soothe Edison. She was also very bright. He had warned her to treat Edison carefully; he was still an angry man.

"Hello," she said, "How's the head?"

"It's fine," said Edison. Then darting a glance at Murray, "and how is your's Miss Jones?"

Murray wanted them to get on. Smiling at Edison's bitter joke he nudged Theora.

"Where do you want to start?" she asked.

"I'll leave you two together. No trouble now or I stop your pocket money," grinned Murray. "You know the rules!"

Edison knew them backwards. And he understood Murray's problem. Murray was the kind who always got to the interview but never quite got the job. Despite himself he growled back. Edison was not a peevish man; but this business had got to him.

"Right," he said to Theora, "you can start by breaking a rule. See what you can access through security on this sudden rash of reporters

being pulled off stories for no good reason. Let's see if you can, sort of, access the inaccessible."

Murray erupted. "Edison leave it. Now back off. I mean it."

He pulled Carter aside. "Edison, look, after the sort of material you normally bring in what's so special about some microwave oven going pop?"

"Since when did people guard exploded microwaves, Murray?"

Murray might have been about to say something when Theora's voice interupted.

"Right. I've accessed the security system as Mr Carter asked. This place is about as inaccessible as I can get."

The two men looked over her shoulder and saw that she has accessed the men's room through the security system. Murray grinned hugely, winked at Edison, and moved away. Theora had broken the tension. Crisis over.

Let's get on with the day.

Edison was impressed. Not only did this girl have a stunning technical capacity, she had nerve and best of all a delicious sense of humour.

"I didn't think that could be done," he said with genuine admiration.

"It can't," Theora replied, "unless you can use the security system against itself. I just made it feed me instead of security. I used to test them. They always failed."

"Human frailty," said Edison. They understood each other perfectly.

"OK Theora, what's on the line apart from dirty pictures?"

They ran through the days' hot stories. Missing missiles, a nuclear waste disposal shuttle gone out of control over Asia, a whole medical team wiped out in South America, a man singing the complete works of Shakespeare for charity. Her screens flickered with constantly updated information. But Edison's eye caught a movement on the screen Theora had inadvertently left on. Someone had walked into the toilet which the securicam was still eyeing mischievously. Edison recognised the faces. Grosman, head of Network 23, and his right hand man, Ben Cheviot.

"Theora, run that will you. And give me sound."

"No problem," she replied

"Listen Ben," said Grosman, Bryce is a problem. Now he's on to this 'Computer Generated People' business he doesn't want to know about Blipverts. He thinks his parrot programme is some sort of breakthrough."

Ben moved to the washbasin. "Unless Bryce can sort Blipverts out they are unusable. You saw that Rebus tape. It is just terrifying."

"Ben, we have no choice. We are committed to use Blipverts with Zikzak. Their contract is massive."

"Massive or not, if this gets out Network 23 is in very serious trouble. They got too damn close to the truth already," echoed the screen.

"Did they now. Theora what's that crew doing on the roof?" said Edison, glancing at her news input screen.

"Ben Cheviot is leaving for New Tokio to sign this big Zikzak contract," she read off her monitor.

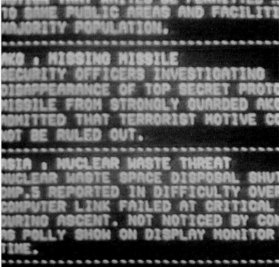

NETWORK 23
4516805976

E.CARTER
XIVHOOX23LM

Edison moved quickly grabbed his camera and shot through the helipad door. Theora had the camera checked, locked and running before he hit the roof.

He emerged as another reporter and crew were interviewing Cheviot.

"This promises to be one of the most momentous contracts in the history of world telecommunications," Cheviot beamed.

As Edison moved in they melted respectfully away. Ben Cheviot paused, mouth open. Edison picked up the conversation with barely a break ... and Theora had it on her screens all the way. Cheviot, almost without faltering resumed his well rehearsed press release. He was still talking when Edison's head moved away from the camera and faced him directly.

"What is the Blipvert problem?" he asked very simply.

Cheviot froze, then recovered enough to begin to object. Then he recognised his questioner.

"Too damn close to the truth already Mr Cheviot?" Edison enquired, innocently.

Ben Cheviot glanced about him.

At her screen Theora watched him with care. What was happening? Carter's story that morning, the sudden cancellation from 'high up', Murray's unusual irritation, Cheviot's patent nervousness ... Edison was on to something alright.

"I have a problem" said Cheviot.

"So I see," responded Edison lightly. Edison switched off his camera. Theora watched the mute screens.

Suddenly Edison's voice cut across the audio link.

"Are you busy tonight Control? Maybe all night?"

Theora paused only for a moment.

"But Mr Carter," she said, "we hardly know each other."

The Tower was alive every hour of the day. Information and entertainment chattered in and out in huge quantities the teleprinter never stopping. But there were times when the tower was switched to auto, when the huge computers ran the night shows and the small teams prepared for the dawn push.

Apart from the routines of maintenance and the constant monitoring of news information and ratings the corridors were empty.

In one section, however, there was a muted glow. Reflected in a screen was the face of Theora. She watched intently. Her eyes moved across the other screens as she monitored the corridors, lifts and rooms around Edison.

Edison was five floors above her moving the final few steps to the door of Bryce's research studio. He had developed great confidence in his new controller. She moved him smoothly and without incident. It was Ben Cheviot's nervous reference to a mysterious "Rebus Tape" that had prompted this break-in.

"I have a problem. I'm at the target but I need the vidilock code to get in."

"I know," responded Theora. "I can see you."

Edison turned to a security camera above him and grinned.

While he reflected on his controller, Theora was busy trying to unscramble Bryce's door code. She programmed some questions – the computer blithely answered. People's birth dates were not secret.

"Hmm. Libra. Might have guessed," muttered Theora as she keyed in her next request and sat back.

Before her tumbled a three dimensional computer graphic array, composed of Bryce's full name, date of birth and department reference. Somewhere inside the resultant cube of letters and numbers might lie a single line which was the selected code. 'Basic isometric coding' she had thought.

"Try BZ2UH," she said quietly.

No go. Edison looked up. But Theora was already spinning the array, probing Bryce's game.

"How about IJ2FI," she said, calmly testing the options.

Edison finger-tipped the panel and as the green light flashed smiled up at the now unseeing camera-for Theora was already switching circuits, checking back down the silent corridors, the hovering lifts ... just in case.

Edison entered a hi-tech world curiously humanised by Bryce's personal effects. Like most studios it was cluttered. Inspiration always seemed to live in chaos Edison reflected, carefully stepping over the paraphenalia of research. He moved through the tiny space between the racks, banks and arrays, his camera under his arm automatically feeding Theora with a roaming tour of the room. Edison found himself in front of a switchboard. He prodded a key hoping to illuminate the gloom The result was immediate and alarming. The lights snapped on promptly followed by a fearsome shriek. He jerked backwards with a crash, then saw it.

It was a parrot in a cage. Beneath it on a large video monitor was the representation of another cage. To his astonishment, as Edison watched, a rudimentary but colourful graphic of the parrot appeared and then animated. It waved its head about, fluttered, and finally and triumphantly squawked.

What intrigued Edison and Theora most was that this was not a picture which recorded the movements of the parrot above it.

It was a computer generated parrot.

Bryce paused. He had spent almost ten minutes mentally trying to calculate the vertical acceleration of a small rubber duck leaping from between his knees and up out of the bathwater. Bryce took to his bath at unusual times. It was one of the few safe places he had. He had almost completed his soapy experiment when a small light blinked on above his bathside monitor. He frowned and poked a panel with the dripping duck.

To his amazement a picture formed with the image of Edison Carter prowling around his studio. Bryce did not waste a nano-second wondering why, or how. He picked up his bathroom handset – a curious machine fashioned like a frog – and punched the keys.

Deep in the many levelled basement of the network tower an armoured van stood amid scattered wreckage. Close by it, poking about among a macabre selection of items was Mahler. Around his waist were strung the plastic bags into which he sorted the severed limbs of accident victims.

Within the van Breughel, his partner, a thin reed of a creature, an insect beside Mahler's blubbery frame-replaced a handset on its rack.

"Yes sir, there will be the usual expenses?"

"Got a nice accident?" asked Mahler, ever eager to ply his trade.

"No, it's the parrot man again."

"Does he want another one? He must eat them by the dozen. Where are we going to get one at this time of night?"

"Not a fresh parrot. A nasty little burglar man. To be cornered and perhaps hit."

These creatures considered themselves one good step above the derelicts. They were self-employed. Not for them the endless, idle stream of the screens. They had purpose in their lives.

But they worked occasionally for Bryce. They hired themselves out for anything 'unusual'. The only question asked, "How much?"

As Breughel and Mahler started the long lift flight upwards Edison had completed his camera check with Theora and was searching with increasing frustration for the tape.

"What is a Rebus anyway?" he demanded, peering under an instrument frame.

Theora responded immediately, "It's some kind of enigmatic picture I think. Mysterious images or something. I'll look it up."

She stared at the screen. Edison was out of shot. All she could see was the bench and the playback unit at which Edison pointed the now stationary camera.

"Have you tried the playback unit?" she suggested.

Edison moved into shot and poked the 'eject' button. A tape slid out. Marked clearly on it was the single word 'Rebus'.

"How did you know?" he said, pushing the tape back in and switching the set on.

"Tell me a kid who ever puts things away," she said, "even clever ones. I know all about little boys."

Edison grinned as he set the camera up to record whatever the screen would reveal on the tape.

"I'll just bet you do," he said.

Edison settled against the cabinet to watch.

Theora watched the screen. Edison's camera had suffered quite a blow during his fight with the derelicts. Was that the reason for that intermittent picture break-up? She carefully selected 'record' on two channels – just in case a record head might go down. She wanted one more check. Edison obliged, trimmed focus, slightly readjusted the angle of the shot and sat back again.

Theora suddenly caught a flash. The picture rolled, flickered then began to stutter. She realised too late that Edison had taken off his headset in order to operate the Rebus tape. Frantically she yelled. But he could not hear her. Nothing she tried could regain that picture, now spluttering with static. The camera was electronically blind.

Edison watched the identification symbols on the studio screen. The tape appeared to be an orthodox sampler of an in-house experiment. One of Bryce's typical perpetual viewers was watching a monitor.

He watched as the symbols shifted. The man stared at the screen, grinning as the 'Polly Show' ploughed on. Then came the Zikzak Blipvert.

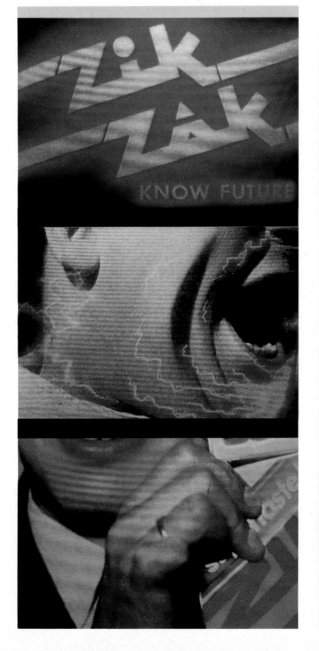

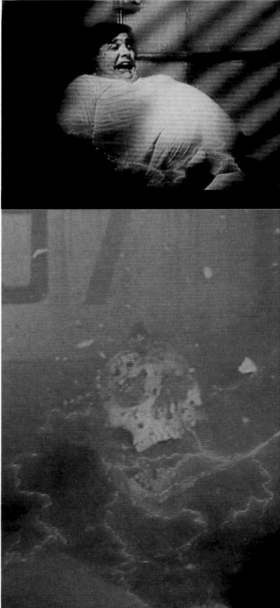

Theora was desperate. The whole point of the break-in was to record whatever was on that mysterious Rebus tape. And now all she had was a crackling snowstorm. She had something else too.

A securicam on a distant part of the same level as Bryce's studio had bleeped a warning, Theora had moments to decide what to do.
The direction in which the two strange men on the screen were moving was clear. Whatever their motive – and by their appearance it was not innocent – Edison was right in their track. She hit the alarm.

Edison stared at the screen. He could barely believe what he had seen. It was horrible. Edison was no stranger to violence and horror; it was his profession to be amongst it. But he had just witnessed a man explode. As he sat, dry mouthed, shaking a little the shrill alarm on Edison's camera shrieked.

Theora heard the bump and rattle on the radio link as Edison rammed on his headset.
"Did you get all that? It was unbelievable."
Theora selected another securicam. Breughel and Mahler were close.
"Look, I'm getting you out of there. Move!" she said. Her instruction was urgent but without panic.

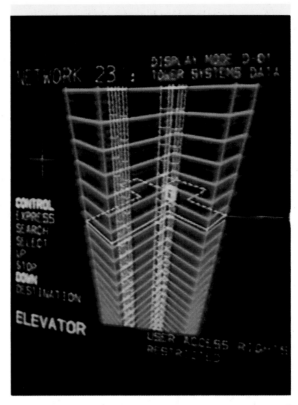

There was no time to discuss the camera fault. Edison was in trouble.

Edison moved. He had learned enough about Theora Jones in the last few hours to know that her instructions were precise and never superfluous. That imperceptible edge in her voice meant business. He was at the lift in seconds.

As his finger jabbed the button the doors parted. Once inside he had barely turned to select the 'down' button when the doors slammed shut and he felt the lift dive for safety. Theora was operating it from her console!

Theora watched her computer graphics record the descent of the lift. She flipped to the lift securicam and found Edison looking up.
"What's the problem control?"
"Intruders. Two. They activated the alarm in the elevator."

She checked their progress. "Oh, by the way," she said quietly, "they're armed."
"Oh great," said Edison with light irony.
Theora read his thoughts.
"They're outsiders Edison. They're not Network men."
She flipped to the securicam in the basement. No movement. Edison felt the lift stop and as the doors slid apart he stepped out.
"Is there a change of plan Control?" he asked.
"No change," came the calm voice of his controller, "I'm standing by for you on the basement camera."
"Well I'm on Level Six," responded Edison, and steppedback into the lift.
Theora glanced at the lift system graphic. Why had it stopped on Six? She checked her keyboard. It was impossible. Then Edison's voice returned. "Look, I don't want to seem difficult but I'm going back up."
The lift was heading right back to level 126. If the intruders were there...
Theora was puzzled. She was entering the right procedures – why had that lift reversed? What had she overlooked? She jabbed her keyboard

and cut up the securicam outside the lift on level 126. She found the corridor clear.

She located Breughel and Mahler moving along the cross corridor. Her instructions were brief, urgent. Edison followed them unquestioningly. She moved him, stopped him, sent him right or left as she played a game of cat and mouse with the advancing strangers. She watched as they moved along, a sinister malevolence smashing its way towards Bryce's studio. The heavy one enjoying the sounds of the shattered busts and pictures he left in his wrecking wake.

Managing with deft moves to place Edison diametrically opposite the two men Theora instructed him to the lift. With that she could spirit him away from the dangerous level again. Edison stood alert at the door, turning away as he heard the crashing approaches of his attackers – for he had no doubt now that he was their target. Behind him he heard the lift doors spring back. He turned and stepped forward: at the same moment that Theora's monitor showed the lift ready to receive him Edison Carter, his fingers clutching the door edge in panic, was staring down a gaping abyss which plunged hundreds of levels down through the howling winds and sickening emptiness of the shaft. He wrenched himself away from the awful edge, shaking with horror ... Theora's finger hit the command key that closed the doors a fraction of a second later ... and in that split second the truth hit her. Someone else was in the system.

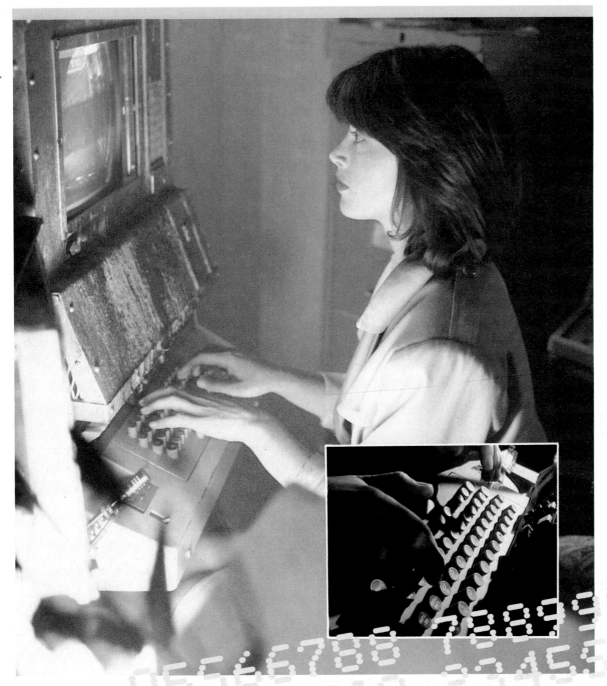

As her hands danced around her keyboard seeking the next move, another pair of hands darted over an identical keyboard.

As she struggled in a perspiring fury to control the system that had Edison now entering a lift and now leaving, hurtling upwards and now plummeting down, another mind gleefully played the same game. Neither player knew the other. Only the commands that ripped between them at the speed of light were known.

And in the eye of the hurricane Edison Carter was pinned to the floor and thrown to his feet, urged in and out of a maelstrom of slamming doors, racing down corridors alive with spinning electronic spies that shrilled his every move. And at every turn the phantoms of the intruders walked.

And suddenly there they were. Two shapes deepening the shadows of the wall.

Edison had been thrown into their path. For one brief moment Theora had lost his trace and left him exposed.

He turned and sprinted back.

Then he recognised a door. He was on the executive level. He pushed through and within moments was standing inside the very men's room from which he and Theora had first overheard Grosman and Cheviot.

Breughel and Mahler paused by the door. Would a man like Carter step into so simple a trap? They knew otherwise – but the sly imperative of their trade bade them inside.

Mahler dropped to the floor, lashing his chain beneath the cubicle doors to snatch at hiding feet. Nothing! Breughel knew as much and turned to continue the pursuit as Mahler's raging chain shattered the ornate mirror on the wall, which, in its reflecting corner, had carried the frozen image of the face of Edison Carter.

Within seconds Edison made the lift, and hurling himself inside came into the anxious orbit of Theora's cameras.

Her fingers flew. In those aching minutes that she had lost Edison she had located a blocking circuit and jammed her opponents input to the lift system – and that diversion would give Theora her move. Now as the lift howled down to the basement she realised that she had won.

Edison erupted from the lift and sprinted across the basement. His eyes, scanning for escape, fell on the beast of a motorbike that was Mahler's private joy.

Not for one second in the past desperate ten minutes had Edison loosened his grip on his camera, and now he jammed it into the rig of the machine and fired up the bike – again and again he pounded the starter until, as in blood red fury his pursuers gained the steps behind him, the great machine growled into life and leaped out of reach.

"My bike!" echoed Mahler's maternal yell.

Edison raced for the exit, his camera recording his flight. Theora watched her screen anxiously as he banked and swerved up the few levels to the exit into the street. But another pair of eyes rode with them, also fed by the same pictures on his own screen.

For the game was not yet over.

As Edison leaned into the final curve the water sprinklers burst above him. He held the throttle open and slewed the machine across the treacherous surface, wrenching it from its slide' and round to face the distant exit.
Theora's pulse rate steadied again as through the sheeting spray she saw the exit looming. But even as she watched, a single finger in a remote room fell upon a key.

Before Edison the black and yellow pantograph exit barrier began to descend.
Theora, sprang forward, fighting to locate and

reverse the command. As Edison, for the first time, saw the approaching danger it slammed up to clearance height. In an instant a new command key was punched and the barrier fell again. As Edison raced to the exit the arm rose and fell as Theora and her opponent arm wrestled the computers to their will. With a triumphant stab at her console Theora saw the arm lock 'up'.

But with a childish flourish, Bryce played the final move.

Edison was within feet of safety when the ramp rose before him. He had the briefest glimpse of the steel ramp hinging up under his front wheel as the bike reared screaming into the air projecting him upwards. His vision was filled with the barrier arm and two words blazing in red.

It was his last image as his head smashed into the arm.

Theora's screen went blank. She was on her feet in moments, running between the rows of control units and racing for the elevator.

In his bath Bryce gave a little laugh. It had been a splendid game and he had, as usual, won. He had a tidy mind in such matters however, and so before returning briefly to the soothing pleasures of his rubber duck he tapped out two terminal instructions.

In the basement the ramp closed back into the floor and the sprinklers obediently stopped – as Theora, soaked and breathless from her running stared at the barrier arm and the splintered sign which read "MAX HEADROOM 2.3 m".

NETWORK 23 : CONTROL MODE: ✻A-1
METRES
2.3
2.0
1.5
1.0

1.8 M
0.0
BARRIER:UP:DOWN:GARAGE EXIT

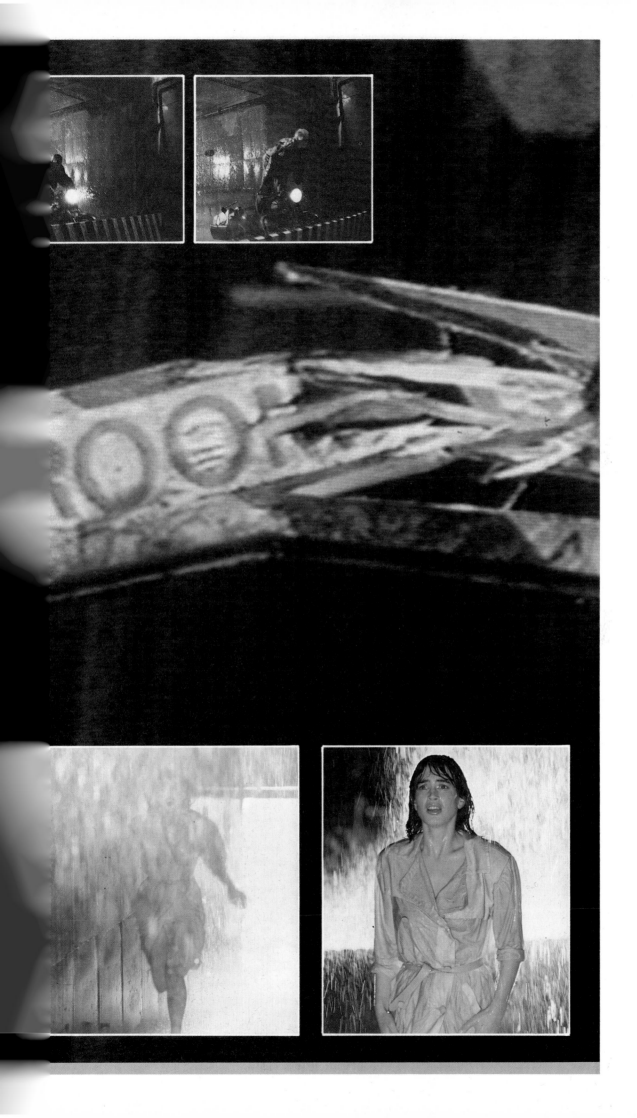

The body of Edison Carter lay in Bryce's studio. He had paid off Breughel and Mahler, and after some thought, put through a call to Mr Grosman.

Grosman had been in his suite half expecting to hear from Bryce. He had hoped to have news on the Blipvert solution.

Now his face stared out at Bryce from the video screen.

"Why?" he said.

Bryce was quite calm. He found it difficult to understand Grosman's anger.

"He saw the Rebus tape."

"Bryce," snarled Grosman, "he is our best known reporter. His show is top rated prime time. He satellites globally..."

"...and he saw the Rebus tape Mr Grosman," cut in a despairing Bryce.

Bryce found this all really trying. The answer was so simple. Carter could be deep frozen, literally kept on ice, in a cryogenic unit. All that Bryce had to do was to run his new scan system on

Carter's brain, compute it, store it, and re-generate it whenever needed. No-one would know he had even gone. It was quite simple. Carter's reports could keep coming in.

"Bryce, I don't want to appear cynical but just *how* do we keep these reports coming in – a seance?"

Bryce tried again."The brain is only a binary computer. A series of on/off switches."

Grosman looked ill. He had his head in his hands. Bryce had noticed people did that and had often wondered why. He tried again.

"You see, Mr Grosman, I can re-create him from my computer. No one will know. But he will in fact be computer-generated. Just like the parrot."

The last image that Bryce had as the video link terminated was the staring eyes of the head of Network 23 and a quavering voice repeating the word 'parrot'.

In the boardroom of network 23 Grosman now paced the floor. His mind essayed the problem. As he tried to assemble his reactions, he was barely aware of the constant chatter of the screens around him, the information that would normally have been the centre of his world.

'...The Arctic War remains in stalemate. The computers predict that no advantage is possible and all parties are standing down. Meanwhile over the Red Sea the two 'Cooler' satellites have drawn a bead on both protagonists on a fourteen hour ultimatum. Unless cancelled by approved peace accords they will autofire simultaneously...'

Grosman moved to the coffee module and spoke into the machine. He waited, his attention caught briefly by the continuing newscast.

'The Zikzak Corporation announced record territory holdings placing them firmly at the top of the superleague of world giants. Nearer home the Streetguards recorded low overnight street crime. Isolated incidents include only 116 murders and 423 assaults. Four more severe domestic explosions finish the roll. These figures citywide and overnight. Next up, market trends...'

Grosman reflected on these explosions. Bryce had better get on top of this Blipvert problem. He decided suddenly that he had better face the boy directly.

As Grosman left the boardroom Theora continued working through the list of accident centres in the city. So far not one had a trace of Edison. It had taken her only minutes to get to the barrier. What on earth could have happened to him. Maybe he was wandering concussed? Once again she repeated his code to the operator – and waited for the reply. She was wet, weary and the stale smell of tobacco that hung around Gorrister's control desk began to irritate her. She was also very worried. And she could not forget that someone else had fought her in the Tower.

Grosman had never previously visited Bryce's studio. He felt uncomfortable. He did not like the sight of Carter either, lying senseless and bloody on the table. He had always thought research departments were clean places.

Bryce had confused him with talk of 'binary computer-brains', 'synaptic breakdown', 'character resonance' and the like. He tried to concentrate.

"So you see Mr Grosman ..."
Grosman also realised that he was irritated by Bryce's inability to pronounce his r's.

"...I can dump down all the information that is in his mind and then retrieve it at will. Then I eliminate any information I don't want. My parrot squawks in just the same way.

But I must have time and money. My research must not be starved."
Grosman recoiled from the thought of the parrot project again.

"Do you ever sleep Bryce?" he asked, half enquiry, half compliment.

"Only physically," said Bryce.

They moved into another part of the studio Grosman was anxious to see results. Talk was confusing. Results mattered.

As Bryce set up the system he explained that he had so far only worked on the head. Not only was the body massively complex to generate, on a television screen only the head was needed. The rest was assumed.

Grosman wasn't so sure.

"I see it as the future Mr Grosman. People translated as data."

"Bryce, does this reproduce Carter here as a reporter is all I'm concerned about? This whole situation is becoming very disturbing."

On a screen before them the rudimentary shape of a head appeared, and slowly built. It was odd. But obviously things were just warming up.

Certainly Grosman was. His first surprise at seeing anything at all gave way to a growing astonishment. He had expected to see Edison Carter on the screen. What he saw was a stuttering image animating erratically.

Bryce saw a new world. He was watching the almost impossible actually working. As he explained excitedly, the circuits were randomising a little, the recall generator was bouncing a bit, and framestore access was imperfect so far, but it worked!

The distance between expectation and enthusiastic conviction has never yet been measured. Grosman expected to see what he had assumed he had been promised. Bryce enthusiastically extrapolated the actual into the potential and then the possible. For him that *was* Carter because a little more time and work and committment would *make* it so.

"Ma ma ma ma mamamama ma max max headroo mamamama ..." jibbered the image.

Grosman stared like a frog facing a watersnake.

"Max Headroom! What the hell? Goddam it! Get that babbling clown off the screen. Kill it. What kind of a screw up is this Bryce? Is this a joke!"

Grosman jabbed at the keyboard

"Leave him alone. Don't you dare touch him."

"Him!" boggled Grosman. "Him? This junk is a machine. It is not Edison Carter. It is a computer generated geek! It is useless. Do you understand me?"

"I understand your *opinion* Mr Grosman, "Bryce retorted.

Grosman chose to miss the barb. "Then understand this. You abandon that garbage. You apply this unit to the crucial matter of the Blipvert problem. I want it resolved and I want it fast. This 'parrot' project terminates NOW!"

Bryce did not react to temperament. Having none he did not recognise it. "Perhaps you don't understand the potential of this development," he persisted.

"I understand the potential of this situation," retorted Grosman, now absolutely certain of his ground. "This electronic oaf has a record of what Carter saw on the Rebus tape. Do you understand that?"

Bryce understood the fact; but not the implication. Of course it knew. It was Carter.

"Smash it," continued Grosman, "smash the thing."

Bryce felt the stirring of an emotion. He would not smash this project nor what it meant. It was a scientific master stroke. It was also many other things which neither Bryce or Grosman had begun to grasp.

Grosman was thinking fast. This machine had a record of what was on the Rebus tape. Fine. Smash the machine. Carter had the same information. There was nothing else to be done. Carter must be disposed of. Then no one outside the board and Bryce would be able to link a few unaccountable domestic explosions with Blipverts. But losing Carter...? Half aloud he muttered, "I do so *hate* wasting an employee."

Bryce watched Grosman.

"I'll have Breughel and Mahler handle it. They relish performing good works."

Grosman stared. He had no choice. At least it kept him well away from anything traceable. He nodded his agreement.

Breughel and Mahler descended the express lift. Between them the inert body of Edison.

Mahler was not keen on Bryce. His cleanliness appalled him. It made him feel uneasy. But he had noticed that he had a well formed head.

"Our Mr Bryce's head would be worth something, eh," he muttered.

"Mm" murmured Breughel. "Not a great payer our Mr Bryce," he said as he examined the fee.

"Nice head tho'" leered Mahler.

Driving through the murky dawn of the city Breughel scanned the monitor. They were always tuned into the body-banks; those not quite official establishments which stored components of bodies that might, very profitably, be sold on to emergency hospital units. The 'donors', or bits of them, usually made their last journey in a van like that of Messrs Breughel and Mahler. Cruising the violent streets they fed on the carrion of the hourly violence which gave them employment.

"Is the body still alive?" queried Breughel from the driving seat.

"He's a bit alive," responded Mahler, struggling to release the camera from Edison's iron grip. Indeed, had Breughel not intervened smartly, his colleague would have smashed the hand to get the camera. As it was the camera remained firmly in Edison's grip.

The best prices were being offered by Nightingales Bodybank. Mahler had a mate there. Specialised in stealing contact lenses. Mahler preferred watches. They weren't as valuable but were less fiddly and not anything like as messy.

At Nightingales they bartered for their price. Breughel checked the papers.

Clinical brain death carried twenty points.

"Is there not a bonus for a live dead body? I mean, he's still warm. Got to be value in that."

"There is," the woman said, "twenty points.

Goodbye."

In the van the two practical men congratulated themselves. They had 'disposed' of the body as instructed and profited by the deal. They had now to find a tertiary bonus.

Bryce had asked them to find a safe storage for his computer generator unit, the device which now contained the rudimentary Edison Carter. It also contained the complete contents of his mind. "He said he wanted it 'safe' and 'in good hands' until he needed it," said Breughel. And he knew some very good, safe and potentially profitable hands.

Dominique was seated at a small table surrounded by papers, ashtrays, glasses and a huge old desk calculator. A handsome woman, she was fighting middle age and winning on points. She thought herself a good organiser – and was wrong. Nevertheless she was a survivor. She ran Bigtime Television because she had no alternative, but she would get her chance one day she firmly believed – and was right.

The premises of Bigtime Television were not vast. They were not hugely expensive. It was in fact an old pink bus. There were good reasons for both those startling facts. First, pink was the colour of the paint they had bought cheap and never bothered to open until they got it home. Second, they needed to be mobile. Because Bigtime Television was a pirate station. Unlicensed, unofficial and largely unwatched it existed by transmitting old video promos years out of date.

Keeping Bigtime running required an engineer, a presenter and a dealer in difficult negotiations of the rougher kind. In Blank Reg, Dominique had all these – and a good if unlikely friend.

Reg was of the Blank generation; that unmanageable group of citizens who had never come within the clinical orbit of the Data Banks.

They appeared on no computer, they had no number, they gave no address – they did not exist, they were unrecorded – the Blanks.

Blank Reg was a punk. He wore a Mohican hairstyle and rancid clothes. He presented an intriguing combination which would have turned not a single head – were it not that Reg was fifty-six years old. And managed to look every one of them. But behind the thuggish exterior, a canny intelligence lurked. Canny enough to be seldom revealed.

Most days, like this one, he opened Bigtime Television to the watching world – a few thousand arid-faced derelicts grouped around the discarded pile of old televisions sets.

So it was that a group of derelicts watched the piled, identical images of Reg as he introduced Bigtime.

" 'Ello," said Reg on twenty sets, "Fine, great, wunnerful."

He switched off the erratically rotating globe which bore the legend 'Bigtime Television'.

"You are tuned into the wired society. This is Bigtime Television day after day making tomorrow seem like yesterday."

Expressionless faces stared at his face crackling over the illegal airwaves.

"You know we said there is no future?" he continued cheerfully, "Well, this is it."

He sat facing a locked-off video camera. Around him the junk heap of the bus studio whined and spluttered. He reached for another old video tape and blew off the accumulated rubble dust.

"Reg," came Dominique's voice from the other end of the bus.

He shushed her as he introduced the next pop promo. " 'Ave a nice day." He turned to her as the music took over.

"Wassup?"

"What is a cross-hatch generator?" she enquired waving a bit of paper.

"Dunno," responded Reg, ever succinct.

"Well we've been billed for one."

"Oh that," he brightened, "probably some bent cabling gear that Poncho slipped me."

Dominique struggled to keep Bigtime vaguely solvent. Reg had no grasp of business. He didn't believe in 'records'. Why not just write down 'money in ... money out' and leave it at that?

Dominique lit another cigarette. Would he never learn? What if a credit terminal demanded her figures – what should she do, wave the back of an old envelope at it!

"Dom, you smoke too much."

"Reg," she snapped, "if you didn't nail your jeans to the floor every night they'd escape. Don't talk to me about personal habits."

God would she ever persuade him to find something other than those old video promos. Being cheap did not mean they were good. Frankly, they were terrible. She didn't want another row. It always ended with Reg looking like a sad, whipped mongrel.

"But Dom," he would whimper, "I *like* them."

She waved a cloud of smoke away and riffled the paperwork. Reg stared at his boots.

"Women," he mused, "always moaning."

His reveries on this timeless theme were interrupted by the spluttering of the vidilock Someone had pressed the buzzer. The vidilock responded. "Hello this is Bigtime Television. Please state your name and code. This – zeerrrup sckreek crackle – Bigtime televveeeeeeee." Reg signalled silence. You never knew who might be out there. They had hidden the bus deep under a cathedral-sized factory ruin ⋯ but you never knew.

Outside Breughel and Mahler watched without emotion as the vidilock squawked and arced its garbled message then ejected its cassette downwards into a bucket of slops which drained the kitchen sink. Mahler reached elbow deep into the liquid refuse and retrieved the tape. He handed it to Reg silently as the door opened.

They had something for Reg. Something special. Him being an expert. It was in the van. Actually they didn't quite know exactly what it was – but it was good value. Reg poked it a few times. There was a silence.

"You press the white button and key things in Reg," offered Mahler.

"Things ..." grunted Reg.

Breughel, master of diplomacy, intervened. "Actually it's the red button."

Reg knew these two. Evil sods. They smelled of their trade. The bargain had time to run.

But suddenly the radio called. Reg wasn't listening as the voice said,

"Nightingales here. The body you sold us has taken a walk."

Breughel moved swiftly.

"Sorry Reg," he weasled, "talk about the business later, eh. Try the goods first sort of thing." He nudged Mahler who was clutching the 'goods' as though his life depended on it. From the look in Reg's eye it probably did.

"Leave it," snapped Breughel. Then quietly, "We have got a deconvenience".

Mahler hugged the machine. It was a bad move. As Breughel crawled off to the driving seat, Reg head-butted Mahler into a brief oblivion.

As the van lumbered away into the drifting smoke of the ghetto and Reg shouldered his mysterious burden, Edison Carter sat shaking and exhausted, in the gutted sepulchre of a vaulted ruin.

He had slipped into consciousness only minutes previously. A hard light had scorched his eyes. Figures moved in the waking nightmare of

a coma. It had taken some moments for him to focus. A great wave of pain and nausea swept over him then he focussed again.

Above him masked green vultures bent and swayed. Something shining moved towards his eyes. He strained to focus – and suddenly saw, inches from his temple, the cold sharp edge of a scalpel moving to his head.

His reaction was unreasoned. Deep in his cortex, instinct took command as he lashed out with lethal power.

As consciousness returned it brought with it pain and shock. Now experience added its measure. He had strength left to move. He must run. Hide. He must find safety. He had got to get to Theora.

He fumbled with his camera. It had not once been released from the grip of his hand. Now battered and bent he begged it to come alive. As he reached to the switch he noticed somethng on his arm. It was a label. It read 'Right Arm. Male. Caucasian. Tissue match 10A67. Freezer 6.'

Theora lay with her hand cradled in her arms. Throughout the night she had exhausted every avenue of enquiry in search for Edison. Finally she had collapsed at her console. She shivered in her fitful doze.

The bright broadcasting dawn was on the city. The Networks accelerated their output. By Theora's head the screen sparkled to life, a musical ident blanding the morning airwaves.

'Following Zikzaks Star Quiz Under the Stars next up Doctor Duncan's Video Sympton Show', a jingle announced the good doctor.

Theora jerked awake. Her monitors rolled empty before her. She turned to the set at her elbow. A middle-aged man stared into her face.

"Doctor Duncan, I've got this terrible anal pustule..."

The cheery bedside voice of the doctor broke in, "Jolly good, drop the trousers and pop the old buttocks against the screen would you."

Theora snapped the set off as the impending posterior loomed before her. She shook her head. God, what time was it? She felt terrible. Then, as she sank back to recover her half dozing sense, the screen before her crackled into ragged life. She tried to adjust the scrambled picture. Then Edison's voice broke through. It was weak, hesitant. "Theora? ... Theora?"

"Edison! Where are you? Keep transmitting I'm trying to locate you."

Edison stared into the lens of his camera. He heard the distorted voice of Theora.

"Theora, I'm in bad shape. I need help."

Theora watched anxiously as the picture settled. To her horror she saw the pale face of Edison as he struggled to speak. Across his forehead a huge, ugly wound. He tried again.

"Theora? Where am I? I need your address quick. I'm in a bad way."

How Edison crossed the city he did not know. Theora's voice guided him as he crept and scurried through the ruined ghettos, using every method she knew to guide him safely. The frail, crackling link which ordered his journey never failed him. But as he reached the door of her apartment and punched in the code his reserves went. He staggered through the door and fell senseless into the calm safety of her bed.

Theora slammed the door of her car and accelerated out of the basement car park, past the shattered sign of the barrier arm, and drove swiftly through the earlylight towards her apartment.

Dominique watched Reg as he poked about inside the machine that Breughel and Mahler had brought. More junk. Reg seemed to spend his life soldering bits of electrical scrap together. He was the limit. "But you don't even know what it is. Might be a bomb. And just what did it cost?"

"Free," smirked Reg, "If it don't work we sling it back."

"If it doesn't work at *what!* Good God Reg! We can't afford decent programmes let alone a cross patch rotovator or whatever it is."

Reg didn't mind Dom moaning. She was doing her best. She was OK. Reg poked a bare wire into a cracked socket. Contact!

"Geronimo!" yelled Reg. "It works."

Dominique scuttled over. They watched as on the screen unfolded a display of data. A rotating graphic of a sort of wire skull spun then resolved itself into a rudimentary head. The head rotated. Stopped. Stuttered and then, unmistakably, became a man's face. it was a sort of animated model, but a face nevertheless. They peered at it. Reg looked blank. Dominique arched a knowing eyebrow. Some junk toy. Typical. Why Reg messed with this sort of...

Her mutterings were halted by a strange noise. From the machine came a disjointed stream of words.

"This is ... .live and direct ... Murray Murray when am I on air ... murr murr ent ent ent enter daa. Enter data..."

Dominique leaned over Reg's shoulder.

He was staring in disbelief and fascination. Whatever this thing was it was incredible. Dominique got to the point swiftly.

"Go on Reg. It wants data. Enter ... Bigtime."

Reg poked at the keyboard. The machine paused, spooled back, then...

"this is ... this is. Big Big Big. This is Bigtime Television? Am I on air?"

They stared speechless at the face. It was talking to them! It was a user-friendly computer-generated head that talked back to you! Reg summed up his astonishment, professional admiration and delight.

"Bloody hell!" he said.

"I beg your pardon," responded the machine.

"Reg it's talking to us," said Dominique. Say something to it. Go on."

Reg considered. What do you say to a machine that talks to you just like a human? I mean, what do you say?

" 'Ullo mate," said Reg. Then added, "I'm Reg, this is my partner Dominique."

Dominique would have protested. Reg really ought to know his place.

'My partner' indeed. One day...

"Hi, hello both of you," said the machine. "Hey Murray do you want to check these ratings, I seem to have an audience of two."

The head smiled. "Welcome to Bigtime — where two's company and three's an audience."

"Where's he *get* all this stuff Reg?"

Reg was in love. This machine was a miracle.

"Un bloody believable," he whispered. It was his highest compliment.

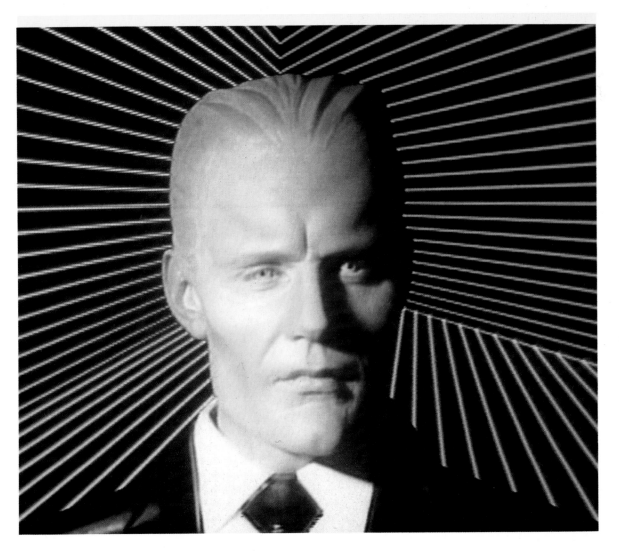

The Boardroom at Network 23 normally operated in a rinsed silence, only broken by polite and discreet debate. As Edison slept and Reg fiddled, the board of Network 23 erupted. Above the pandemonium Grosman's voice bellowed.

"Chaos ... is ... not ... helpful! Please be seated." He waited for a servile calm to return.

"Now Ben, what exactly did Zikzak say in New Tokio?"

Ben Cheviot spoke calmly and without rancour.

"Their whole campaign is organised around the use of our Blipverts to prevent channel switching. No Blipverts — no deals."

Ms Formby spoke firmly. "This contract is huge. We cannot just reject a transglobal campaign. We *cannot* withdraw Blipverts now!"

"We can't go on using them!" exclaimed Ben, "They're lethal godammit!"

"That isn't proved," said Edwards.

Ashwell felt he needed to make a point. Good for the record. Lighten the proceeding. Show Grosman he could calm these types down.

"If that tape wasn't proof," he chortled, "what do you need — a live demonstration, ha, ha."

"I find that tasteless. Grosman snapped." He scoured the table with his eyes.

"Bryce's Blipverts are a brilliant breakthrough: half a minute of advertising in three seconds. It is magnificent!"

"It is," Ben Cheviot interrupted. "it is also killing people."

Grosman snarled back. "We buried that kind of crap decades ago. Dammit, I am not going to risk my network over it! Ben, I am talking ratings."

"And I am talking people," said Ben calmly.

"Same thing!" said Grosman.

Then Ben Cheviot put himself out on the ramparts. From this point he stood alone.

"We're coming clean on this," he said. "If you don't ... I will."

Grosman froze. Not a muscle stirred on his face. Not an eye blinked or wavered in the terrible cold stare that now lay on Cheviot. Barely did his lips move as he spoke, his meaning chillingly clear.

"I really wouldn't do that Ben."

Theora had dozed beside Edison. He hadn't stirred. Even when she dressed the head wound he had not moved.

Now she stood with a cup of freshly made coffee, deep in thought. What had happened to him? Who on earth was in the computer at the Network? Who were the two intruders and who had sent them – and who had spirited Edison away to wherever he had been? She remembered with a shiver that when she found Edison on her bed he still had a tag, like a crazy earring, dangling from his right lobe. It read, 'Head. Male. Tissue match 10A67. Freezer 14.'

"If you're making coffee I'd appreciate one."

She started, then turned. "I thought you were asleep."

"I make a habit of that."

An hour later he was showered, fed and relaxed a little. He was still absorbing Theora's apartment.

He read through the teleprinter news.

"Hey Theora, what's a Mitzoguchi ... was that shoes or a motor cycle?"

"Neither, he was a Japanese film director."

"Oh. How's the cold?"

She came over with the camera, plonked it on the table. "Fine. How's the head."

Edison grinned. It hurt but it was worth it. She was spectacular.

"Edison, can't you remember *anything* about the Rebus tape?"

"Nothing. I remember the car park, the barrier arm and then voices that – I don't know, could have been Bryce and Grosman – then some creep bending over me with a scalpel. Otherwise. Nothing."

"I'm sorry. We need that tape. I still don't know why the pictures broke up. The camera is OK now, it was just contacts. What was on that tape Edison?"

"I don't know and whatever it is someone doesn't want me to find out."

Theora pondered. "Well, whoever was in the system last night knew what they were doing. I nearly lost you."

"Well," said Edison, "you can have the chance to lose me again tonight. I'm going back into Bryce's studio."

Then it happened again. The head agitated. A computer graphic of a corridor, a lift, an exit barrier from a carpark and then the picture locked. A sign, 'Max Headroom 2.3 m' filled the screen.

"What the hell is that?" asked Dominique.

"His ratings?" suggested Reg, "2.3 million?"

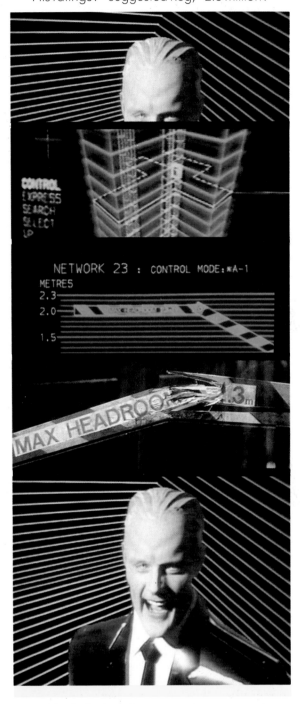

Reg was under the bus wrestling with a sagging exhaust pipe. He had lost the bout and was crawling out when he heard Dominique yell. "Hey come quick." He sat bolt upright and cracked his head on the chassis. He gave a yelp of pain. Reg rushed to the front of the bus. A crisis. Trouble. He barrelled round to the door.

Dominique was jubilant. "We've got a client Reggie darling."

Reg didn't react.

It seemed that a local televison repair unit had seen the talking head and it struck them that it would make a useful advertisement for their repair service. Dominique was delighted.

"He goes on the blink too much," protested Reg.

"But that's the *point*," she replied. "They love that." She grinned from earring to earring. It was incredible.

The Head was babbling again. The ratings showed a hundred viewers.

"A hundred viewers," said the head. "Wow, what am I supposed to do? Get stage fright?"

Then came the stutters. Reg leaned close, trying to work out why this kept happening. He knew little enough about the machine but this was odd – almost as if it was trying to access something it couldn't quite reach. Almost as if it had, well, it sounded crazy, but ... lost its memory. Reg dismissed the thought.

Suddenly the head responded, "Bigtime! this is Max Headroom on Bigtime Television and what I want to know is: don't eskimos ever get bored with their weather forecasts?"

"It's amazing. I just can't believe it's possible," mused Dominique as Reg gazed in awe at his new machine.

"And another thing I want to know: if you're all watching me who's watching Network 23? The network with a great future behind it. As they say when you're buying suppositories, 'With friends like those behind you who needs enemas?' "

Reg was overwhelmed. Whatever this thing was it was magnificent.

"Go for it Max," he murmured to himself, "go for it – you son of a bitch!"

Max Headroom was born. Across the sad ghettos his face flickered on a thousands screens. This weird, funny, erratic, unpredictable, inconoclastic figure tickled the parched imaginations of the thousands of derelicts who gathered for warmth around the video camp fires of the city.

Nobody asked or cared *what* he was only *that* he was. And he was good to have around. The word kept spreading.

In his studio, the seated figure of Bryce stared at Breughel. The standing figure of Breughel stared at Mahler. Mahler shifted uneasily and stared at his feet. They weren't getting very far.

Bryce had previously been trying to contact them for hours. They had not responded. It was difficult for them to explain it away by saying that they were chasing someone they had been paid to kill, and not quite getting paid for selling something they had been paid to keep safe.

It was all very negative convenience-wise.

Breughel made a vain attempt to pretend radio failure – a fried micro-chip. Mahler was inspired by the thought they had popped round to see his sick mother. Bryce for all his lack of years X-rayed through their pathetic stories.

"You did exactly as I asked?" he queried carelessly.

"To the letter," Breughel responded.

"One got rid of and the other locked away."

Bryce kept his eyes on them. They were not the sort of eyes that pin strong men to walls or cause wild beasts to whimper. But they were powerful, not in themselves but in which head they sat.

"Oh good," said Bryce. "Locked away. I admire the precision and clarity of your response. Perhaps therfore you could clearly and precisely explain *this?*" He reached out and flipped a channel selector. Loud, clear and unmistakable came the voice of Max Headroom.

"Do the Chinese really have thirty ways of saying one little word, 'love', and is that why their population is so big? You know ..."

Mahler, rather brightly, pointed out that the strange face was very much like 'that other bloke'. He wondered if it was a film of him. Breughel was putting two and two together very fast. Bigtime. That box.

"It *is* very like that other bloke but it is not a film," said Bryce warming to his uneasy audience. "That, Mr Mahler, is a complete person. In that machine is the coded mind of the dead Mr Carter."

Mahler's feet shifted again. Breughel looked straight ahead.

"Soon," Bryce went on, "I will be able to reconstruct *anybody* on a screen. Even you Mr Mahler, so accurately that even your mum would think it was you."

Mahler nodded dumbly, disturbed at the awesome prospect but rather missing the point.

Breughel missed nothing. Neither the point nor its implications.

"You might care to call it The Phoenix, Mr Bryce," he ingratiated. "My word, all your politicians in little boxes."

"Very handy," Breughel mused.

Bryce recognised too late that Breughel was intelligent. Bryce had always assumed that he was simply inhumanly greedy, easily manipulated and usefully vicious. He had just learned something, and an indiscrete few seconds too late.

"Now," he said, resuming a hopeless authority, "exactly where is Bigtime Television?"

Network 23 was buzzing with rumour. Everyone could see the ratings dip. There wasn't a screen in the building which didn't carry the information. Everyone knew that Blipverts had been suspended 'over some contractual detail.'

Rumour had it that the board was in emergency session.

Rumour has many tongues, and six of them were wagging furiously across the table of the boardroom.

"We could move up the Polly Show, pull in an extra episode and get the standbye show on line..." suggested Formby.

"And we'd have a vacuum by midnight." scoffed Edwards.

"We could re-run the Rat Killers. It went megabucks last global." offered Ashwell, keen to please.

"We could go porno early," said Formby. Ashwell had often wondered about Formby.

Grosman moved to the point. "What did it Ben – what do the analysts say?"

Cheviot, calm, reasonable, replied, "It's only two percent."

"Two percent of our ratings is twenty-six million consumers Ben. Once they start switching channels it's war, you know that."

Ben tried to dampen the situation, but other politics held sway. Those who had opposed Ben when he demanded the withdrawal of Blipverts – and had finally got his way by diplomacy and a courageous stand – now sniped cunning, with their eyes on Grosman.

Grosman chose.

"I am going to reinstate Blipverts. And that's final."

There was no sign of strain at Bigtime Television, unless you counted Reg's struggle with the lid of a food tin as stress. Dominique was gushing.

"Reg, I take it all back darling, you're brilliant. Just look at these figures! This Max thing will keep you in beer tokens for ever."

Reg was prising the lid of his tin back with what in him amounted to fervour.

"I'm starving," said the dedicated Reg, "I'm going to micro some alphabetti spaghetti letters in tomato sauce. You want some?"

"Do me a favour," postured Dominique. She was sipping some rather fine wine, drawing on an emperor sized cigarette and tinkling like a Christmas tree in new, very expensive, earrings and a diamond brooch shaped BT.

Reg was in a reflective mood. He dug into the cold tin and chewed on the hieroglyphic pasta.

"You know, this Max has got a weird facility. His datastore is huge, right?"

Dominique supposed so. But so what?

"He can access a load of info, right. Key in a command – and away with the mixer. But, see, he doesn't just build data, you know: 2,4,8,16,32. He jumps. And it's not random Dom. It's more than information. It's like intuition."

Dom was lost. Anyway what did it matter. Max was just a voice box and a computer with a lot of bytes. Root it and off it would go.

"It's only other people's phrases he uses Reg!"

He paused, a mouthful of vowels and consonants.

"Oh yeh," he said slowly, "then how come he's got a sense of humour?"

Reg was convinced that there was something very bent about all this. Breughel and Mahler having him in the first place. Way out of their league. Didn't add up. And a darker thought had been troubling him.

"What if the real owner wants him back?"

Dominiqe wasn't going to lose her golden egg producing goose.

"Over my dead body," she snorted.

"It might be," replied Reg.

There was a long pause. Dominique shifted uncomfortably and looked at Reg with a sudden unease.

Reg put down his tin. "I'm going to put the wheels back on the bus. Just in case."

Reg's instincts were sound. Had he known what had happened in the last few hours that evening he would have had the wheels on and the engine running.

While he and Dominique had puzzled and rejoiced over Max, Edison Carter had indeed returned to Bryce's studio. This time Theora had brought every securicam in the building under her command. Nothing would move without her knowing.

Her first discovery was that Bryce's studio was not empty. At first she thought that they were confounded once more in their quest for that elusive Rebus tape, but then very softly and delicately she eased the studio securicam round. To her initial dismay she found herself looking at Bryce. He was experimenting with his parrot.

The information was with Edison only a corridor away in an instant. He moved to the studio door.

Theora blocked the Level 126 lift command circuits. Nothing could now stop on that floor. Edison tapped in the code once again. In moments he was inside, creeping very quietly towards the sound of a jibbering parrot.

Bryce had fiddled with the Blipvert system but soon got bored. Maybe he would get an assistant onto it. Although why all the fuss he couldn't say.

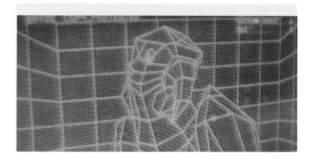

He had turned instead to his parrot project. He knew he had something so unique, so intricately clever that he was determined to perfect it. He had no idea that what he was developing might be one of the most significantly lethal advances of all time.

Had it occurred to him he would simply have sat down to calculate all the ways in which these devices might entirely replace people. He would not have pondered the result of having people where no real people were – unlike Mr Breughel: "All you politicians in little boxes. Very handy." Mr Breughel had swiftly seen that whoever controlled those boxes...

But such thoughts were far from Bryce's mind as he stared at his screen and worked diligently away to perfect his parrot. It was only when he flipped the screen off to change programmes that he found himself staring at the perfect and very real reflection of Mr Edison Carter.

Edison was not an insensitive man. But faced with the author of his previous nights anguish he wasted no time. When he left he had learned everything there was to know about the Blipvert problem. And made very certain that Bryce would not trouble him again for a few hours. With Theora's help it took little time to locate the source of the transmission of Max Headroom and the little box that contained the stolen mind of Edison Carter.

At precisely the same time, in the boardroom of Network 23, great sighs of relief were being heaved by the Executive. They had worked in a frenzy to steady the wildly oscillating ratings of the channel. The reinjection of Blipverts had eventually dampened the swinging allegiances of the consumers. The channels had ceased to switch against the Network. Others had begun to take the fall. It had been close. But they had triumphed.

"That was unpleasant," Grosman had said in an uncharacteristic show of emotion.

"Not half as unpleasant as it will be when people start reacting to blipverts," Ben had said to derisive groans.

"Somebody, sometime, is going to make the connection."

Ben was right. And that connection was being made faster than he thought.

But for now they had relaxed. Ben was just oversensitive. Hadn't the guts for the job. Best ignore him.

Ashwell, searching as usual for a chance to demonstrate his skills, had been eyeing the ratings screen which dominated the end of the room. All eyes had been gauging the movements at the peak of the graphs; the troughs had remained ignored. But he had noticed a startling movement in the figures of an unknown minor station. It was a chance to show his alertness.

"Hey, look at this," he said. "That climb is exponential."

They all turned to follow his gaze. There on the screen the graphic representation of Bigtime Television advanced and retreated, then moved steadily upwards.

Edwards, statistician and creep, dismissed the move as trivial.

"The figures are minute – down in the thousands," he mocked.

Ms Formby felt they should take a look anyway. If nothing else, it was worth seeing what was causing this surge. Network 23 might find something worth chasing.

The channels flipped and the digits flew. Seconds later a strange figure occupied the screen.

"Now I understand why people prefer watching television to radio: they've worked out how boring it is watching the radio," it said.

There was an appreciative chortle from the executives. There was something endearing about the rich yet laconic timbre of his voice. It verged on parody but remained controlled and sharp. He had a winning smile, a plastic pastiche of the comic presenter.

"This is Max Headroom on Bigtime Television."

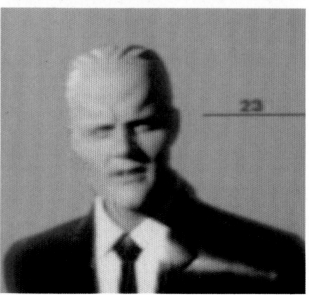

"I had to spend a little time recently with a parrot. It's true! I won't tell you why, but what amazes me is that anyone should want to spend any time at all sitting at home teaching a bird to talk ... I mean what's wrong with the rest of the family, uh?"

They all found it very funny. It wasn't so much what he said but the self-deprecating confidence with which he spoke.

But amid the light relief one face stood out in profound contrast. Grosman stared at the screen. The colour had drained from his face, and his mouth was clamped shut. As he glared up at this electronic phantom Grosman felt a nausea deep in the pit of his stomach. That face, that damnable face! It was the same perverted image of Edison Carter that he had seen the night before – and had ordered destroyed!

When he found words there were but three. Each sounded like a single death sentence.

"GET ... ME ... BRYCE."

He left the boardroom in an explosion of fury. Within minutes he and his personal security guards had burst into the studio. Grosman stared down at the bound and gagged figure of Bryce, lashed whimpering to his chair. Grosman seized the tape that secured Bryce's mouth firmly shut. Bryce gave a shrill scream as he ripped it violently from his lips.

"Now Bryce," he hissed, "WHERE ... IS ... IT?"

Bryce whispered, terrified.

"That pirate station ... I think ... I think Edison Carter might have it."

Grosman blinked once. His mind rumpused with disbelief.

"Carter? But you told me he was..."

Suddenly he knew. Very suddenly the whole awful truth reared up before him like armagedon.

"Who did this to you?"

Bryce had only one word to say. He knew that when he spoke it the world would end ... and if not, at least the roof would cave in.

"Carter," he spluttered.

Grosman turned an unusual hue. The two menacing aides flexed their fingers. The parrot turned away.

Grosman lunged at Bryce, wrenching him with terrible strength clean out of the chair. He pinned him to the steel cupboard door, his eyes staring garroted from his sweating face.

"How do we find it? How? Damn it!"

"Breughel and Mahler," whispered Bryce. "They know."

Minutes later at almost the same instant two vehicles began to move. From the bowels of Network 23 Breughel's van roared away. Within it, crouched among the grotesque artifacts of a gruesome trade, Grosman and Bryce hung grimly on. The two huge protectors of the head of the Network sat in a brutish misery of ruined suits, their piggish eyes hidden behind the dark blank surfaces of their sunglasses. From the front of the vehicle came wistful demented singing. Breughel's madness floated tunefully back to them.

From the dark protective arches of the ruin, Bigtime Television lurched and bellowed across the uneven ground. There had been no time to prepare. As the bus took flight it tore the still live power cables clean from the wall in great crackling sheets of sparks.

The passengers in Breughel's van remained uncomfortable. But their discomfort would have been even greater had they been privileged with the view of the road ahead. For as Breughel and Mahler continued their inane duet they saw coming towards them through the half light a great swaying pink bus, across it boldly emblazoned the legend 'Bigtime Television'. Before Mahler could speak Breughel silenced him with a glance. He had been thinking very hard.

All these important people chasing the Max box could only mean that there was something very special about it.

It must be very valuable.

Breughel made his decision.

The van bounced on deep into the ruined sector of the city towards the point where Bigtime Television had been so effectively hidden. Breughel knew this crumbling warren well and had long ago mastered its lethal tracks.

It was the ideal place in which to do his business. People might arrive or disappear without trace or question. In its dark wet miles inhabited by derelicts no official powers ventured.

Breughel drove over the fresh imprints left by the pink bus minutes before, crushing the abandoned slop bucket and passing the still spluttering cables swaying from the walls.

The van turned into a small blind alley its lights picking out the smooth wall at its end and ranging over the long blind windows and empty doors. But they did not catch the sharp movement as two figures slipped swiftly into the shadows as the beam swung across the wall in a tight arc.

Breughel reversed to within a few steps of the wall.

Mahler opened the two rear doors and assisted Grosman and Bryce out into the clammy night. Moving a step or so behind them he asked the two emerging aides to "Close the door lads". It was a friendly request. But his eyes never left the image of Breughel's face staring at him in the reflecting driving mirror. As the doors banged shut in unison he nodded suddenly.

Breughel slammed the armoured van into reverse and hurtled backwards. Only half a cry escaped the two men as they were crushed and splintered into the brick wall.

The van jerked forward. Grosman and Bryce gaped in horror as the two wrecked bodies were lifted into the van. Waste not want not. Here was a little more profit for Nightingales Bodybank.

As the mangled remains of his guards were dragged off Grosman's hand found Bryce's. Stunned like rabbits, they backed towards an adjacent opening, longing for the protective cloak of the damp shadows. With only half a step between them and deliverance they heard a slight noise. Very close.

A harsh light snapped on. They stood blinded by a wall of blue light.

And from behind it came a voice.

"Don't move! You're not going *anywhere.*"

Edison Carter stood facing them. At his side a sun gun held high by Theora. Grosman froze again as he heard the voice continue.

"Murray, are you getting this?"

Murray was in the control room. He listened to Carter in astonishment. When Carter cleared the line Murray knew that there was only one man he could turn to with the biggest story his newsroom had ever handled.

And so it was that Ben Cheviot was seated in Grosman's place in the empty, humming boardroom at the end of the telephone which was even now in Murray's hand.

"You realise what this means? You want to transmit?" Murray asked, leaning over the monitor which carried the startled faces of Grosman and Bryce as they blinked into Carter's accusing lens.

In the following pause Grosman knew he still had the upper hand. He was the head of Network 23. The channel could never, and would never, permit this story to be tranmsmitted live, now, or at any other time. It would mean the end of himself and very possibly the Network. The crucial investments of the mighty Zikzak Corporation would evaporate and with them a thousand other sponsors. Grosman was certain that Carter would be stopped.

"It'll never happen Carter. They won't transmit it."

Murray heard Grosman. He too knew that the decision was terrible in its implications.

"What do I do Ben?" he asked. My God, he thought, what can any of us do?

The answer came after the briefest hesitation. The voice was calm. "Do what you have to Murray."

Murray reached out, hesitated, and then pressed the red button.

"We interrupt this programme for a special newsflash. For the details, over now live and direct to Edison Carter"

Grosman stared out of the screen like a goosed goldfish.

"Mr Grosman, head of Network 23, you are going to tell me exactly what I want to know about Blipverts. The whole story."

The world watched. Linking announcements had been flashed to hundreds of networks. A thousand satellites fed countless millions of news-hungry television sets across the endless electronic horizons of the globe, obediently relaying the words and pictures from that one small, deadly video camera in Edison's hands.

"Tell me sir," Edison began as a great silence fell upon the watching world. "When did you first learn that your Blipverts caused people to ... spontaneously explode?"

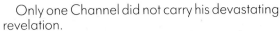

Only one Channel did not carry his devastating revelation.

Bigtime Television swayed and bounced through the night. In the cabin Dominique clung tipsily on to the driving seat, a precious brimming glass spilling a cascade of wine at each lurch.

Behind her the voice of Max Headroom chattered happily on.

Blank Reg, peering into the night, reached out to the monitor switch in front of him as Edison's voice asked that terrible question.

"What a load of bollocks!" said Reg.

Bigtime Television sped away with its most precious cargo safe inside. They had Max Headroom. Every minute that passed put them and their glittering prize closer to the enveloping safety of a place only Reg knew.

But had Reg looked behind him he would have seen a small, furtive van tracking them as a wolf might stalk a sheep. Two grim and sinister figures sat in it, and at its back two doors glistened with traces the colour of blood.